MISUNDERSTANDING COMICS

WRITING
**Tim Heiderich
& Mike Rosen**

ART
Mike Rosen

VARIANT COVER/
INSIDE COVER
Jennifer Albright

SPECIAL THANKS
**Jennifer Albright
Terisa Green
Jim Higgins**

Fonts:
ACME Secret Agent
BadaBoom
Marker Felt. (Don't laugh.)

ISBN-13: 978-0-9910097-0-1

This is a work of parody.

First Printing Oct. 2013

Funded entirely by our generous KICKSTARTER backers.

www.MisunderstandingComics.com

Printed somewhere in China

CONTENTS

INTRODUCTION

WITH THANKS + APOLOGIES TO
SCOTT MCCLOUD

WE COULD NOT HAVE DONE THIS
TERRIBLE THING WITHOUT YOU.

INTRODUCTION

STUPID, TINY FEET...

HI, COMICS READER! I'M COMIC BOOK LEGEND *SKETCH McCLOUDMOUTH!*

SO, YOU WANT TO LEARN ALL ABOUT SEQUENTIAL ART?

UNDERSTANDING SEQUENTIAL ART MEANS SEEING HOW EACH PIECE ACTS AS A WINDOW INTO AN ARTIST'S SOUL.

THEY WEAVE STORIES THAT REACH ACROSS DIFFERENT CULTURES, ENRICHING THE LIVES OF PEOPLE OF ALL AGES!

IT COMBINES THE ABSTRACT IDEAS OF WRITING WITH THE VISUAL STORYTELLING OF ART!

...OR WOULD YOU RATHER DRAW HOT CHICKS WITH GIANT BOOBS? SUPERHUMAN GLADIATORS KICKING ASS AND DROPPING AWESOME ONE-LINERS?

DO YOU WANT TO MAKE A FAT STACK OF CASH?

THEN YOU DON'T WANT TO LEARN ABOUT *ART.*

YOU WANT TO LEARN ABOUT *COMICS.*

MISUNDERSTANDING COMICS

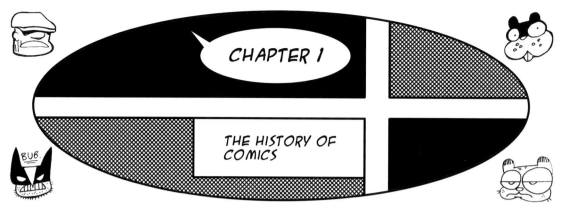

CHAPTER 1

THE HISTORY OF COMICS

SEQUENTIAL ART IS A YOUNG ART FORM, AND NEW KINDS OF ART RARELY GET ANY RESPECT. *FINE ART* IS WHAT'S KEPT IN MUSEUMS, LOOKED AFTER BY CURATORS WITH PHD'S. IT'S HUNDREDS IF NOT *THOUSANDS* OF YEARS OLD!

WHEREAS *COMICS* HAVE BEEN SOLD IN DRUGSTORES AND TOY SHOPS, TO CHILDREN AND TO CHILDLIKE ADULTS. YOU CAN'T GET MUCH MORE DIFFERENT THAN THAT!

SHH!

VENUS OF WILLENDORF

JUDITH BEHEADING HOLOFERNES

DAVID

BUT WHAT SEPARATES *FINE ART* FROM *COMICS?*

WILDDOGS

NOT MUCH! PEOPLE HAVE LIKED *NUDITY,* *SEX* AND *VIOLENCE* FOR AGES!

THERE'S A LOT IN COMMON BETWEEN *ANCIENT ART* AND *MODERN COMICS*.

AND THAT'S *TERRIBLE!*

THIS *EGYPTIAN PICTOGRAPH* OF A *GRAIN HARVEST* IS FROM 4000 B.C.* -- AND IT READS JUST LIKE A COMIC STRIP!

*THAT'S AS MANY AS FORTY CENTURIES!

BUT THE EGYPTIANS READ ZIG-ZAG FROM *BOTTOM* TO *TOP!*

EVEN THE *MAYA* HAD A VISUAL LANGUAGE FOR THEIR MANY LEGENDS!

THIS STORY DEPICTS THE HERO *CRUMMY* WORSHIPPING THE BIRD-HEADED GODDESS *QUETZALCOATL.*

HE ASKS *MISTER NATURE* HOW TO SEDUCE HER, AND, UH...

I CAN'T REALLY TELL *WHAT'S* GOING ON HERE.

READ THIS ONE TOP TO BOTTOM, LIKE A NORMAL PERSON!

...BUT ENOUGH ABOUT VIOLENCE.

LET'S TALK ABOUT **SEX!**

SEX IS **BIG**, AND HAS BEEN SINCE A HORNY CAVEMAN CARVED THE CORPULENT **VENUS OF WILLENDORF** OVER **22,000** YEARS AGO!

SKRITCH SKRITCH SKRITCH

WE CAN'T BE SURE **WHAT** THE STONE TOTEM WAS USED FOR --

BUT JUST **LOOK** AT THAT **FIGURE!**

SHLICK SHLICK SHLICK

SMOOCH!

KISS KISS

smack

AHEM!

BUT **BEAUTY** STANDARDS HAVE CHANGED

SO LET'S IMPROVE HER, TOO!

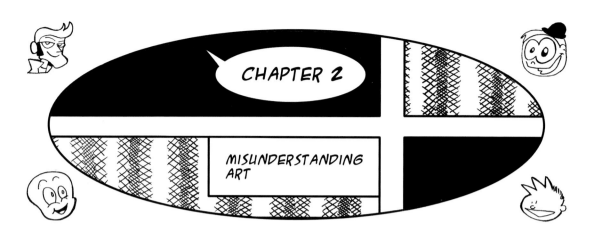

CHAPTER 2

MISUNDERSTANDING ART

AN ARTIST'S STYLE SAYS A LOT ABOUT THEM, AND ABOUT THE VISION OF THE WORLD THEY ARE TRYING TO COMMUNICATE.

THE *HARD, ANGULAR* LINES OF DICK TRACY CREATE A STRONG-JAWED HERO FIGHTING CLEAR, OBVIOUS *VILLAINY.*

GIG'S UP, YA MUGS!

THE OPEN AND *FRIENDLY* FACES OF A KIDS' COMIC ARE *RELAXING* AND *COMFORTING.*

THE *JAGGED* LINES AND *SPLATTER* OF GRITTY DETECTIVE COMICS CAN CREATE A FRENZIED, UNCERTAIN, AND *CHAOTIC* FEELING IN THE READER.

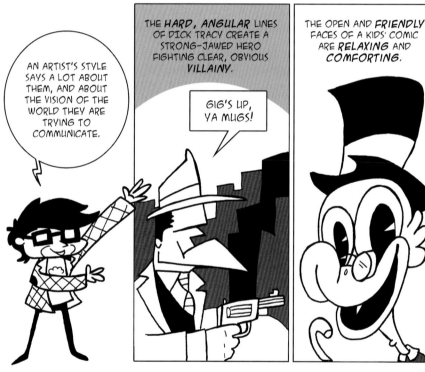

BUT WHY SHOULD ONLY TALENTED, HARD-WORKING ARTISTS GET ALL THE RECOGNITION...

WHEN READERS JUST WANT SOMETHING TO JERK OFF TO?

THE DEATH OF BREASTELLA!

BUT *OVER-INDULGING* IN *SPLASH PAGES* CAUSES THEM TO LOSE THEIR *IMPACT!*

AND SHOWING EPIC *ART* WITHOUT ANY *SUBSTANCE* IS RATHER, WELL...

LAZY.

IT'S EASY TO CONFUSE THE **CONTENT** YOU CREATE WITH THE **FORM** IT TAKES.

CONTENT IS THE *MEANING* BEHIND YOUR WORK, WHILE FORM IS HOW **COOL** IT LOOKS.

AND SINCE FORM IS THE *FIRST* THING A READER SEES, THAT MEANS IT MATTERS THE *MOST!*

THE RIGHT *FORM* CAN ADD A TOUCH OF CLASS TO YOUR *CONTENT.*

ADORN YOUR BORING CONTENT WITH ENOUGH *FANCY TRINKETS* AND YOU'VE IMPROVED THIS WEAK SAUCE WITH YOUR OWN BRAND OF *STYLE.*

IT LOOKS SO GOOD, WHO *WOULDN'T* WANT TO DRINK IT?

SIP!

PTUI!

AN ARTIST'S STYLE IS DEFINED NOT JUST BY THEIR TALENT, BUT BY HOW MUCH THEY'RE SHOWING OFF ...OR HOW LAZY THEY ARE.

SEE IF YOU CAN RECOGNIZE THESE ARTISTS BY THEIR, AHEM, "STYLE"!

1. SO YOU THINK YOU'RE A GOOD ARTIST? HOW MANY AWARDS ARE NAMED AFTER YOU? *2.* LUSH SCENERY, EXOTIC WOMEN AND "HOW TO SPOT A JAP". *3.* CREATES THE MOST VIVID, REALISTIC WORLD, BUT CAN'T DRAW A BOY ADVENTURER. *4.* CANKLES AND BIG BUTTS. *5.* ALL CHARACTERS, IDEAS AND ARTWORK © STAN LEE *6.* A 3000 PAGE MANIFESTO ABOUT MY DIVORCE. *7.* CTRL-C, CTRL-V *8.* LIVING IN STERANKO'S DOUBLE-PAGE SPLASH SHADOW. *9.* NOT SURE IF THIS IS TEZUKA OR OTOMO... I GOTTA BE HONEST, THEY ALL LOOK ALIKE TO ME. *10.* TRACED FROM PORNO. *11.* AN ARMY OF UNCREDITED INTERNS. *12.* IF YOUR ART LOOKED LIKE THIS, YOU'D BE DEPRESSED, TOO. *13.* "I SHALL DESTROY ALL CIVILIZED COMIC BOOK ARTISTS!" *14.* I DREW THIS WHILE DAYDREAMING IN ENGLISH LIT. *15.* I'M TOO ANGRY TO LEARN TO DRAW! *16.* MANLY MEN HAVE BREASTS BIGGER THAN THEIR HEAD. *17.* CRUDE AND BRUTAL -- AND THAT'S JUST THE POLITICS. *18.* A TOTALLY REALISTIC WORLD WHERE THE WOMEN HAVE HUMONGOUS KNOCKERS. *19.* IT ISN'T THE ART IN THIS TRACT THAT'S UGLY -- IT'S THE MESSAGE. *20.* THIS SELF-PUBLISHED COMIC ABOUT CHURCHGOING WITCHES THAT YOU WILL NEVER POSSIBLY READ IS REGISTERED WITH THE LIBRARY OF CONGRESS. *21.* THE ARTIST FURRIES DESERVE. *22.* THE VOIGHT-KAMPFF TEST OF COMIC STRIPS. *23.* I HAVE NO DRAWING TALENT AND NOTHING TO SAY. HERE'S MY WEBCOMIC.

SHOW-OFF

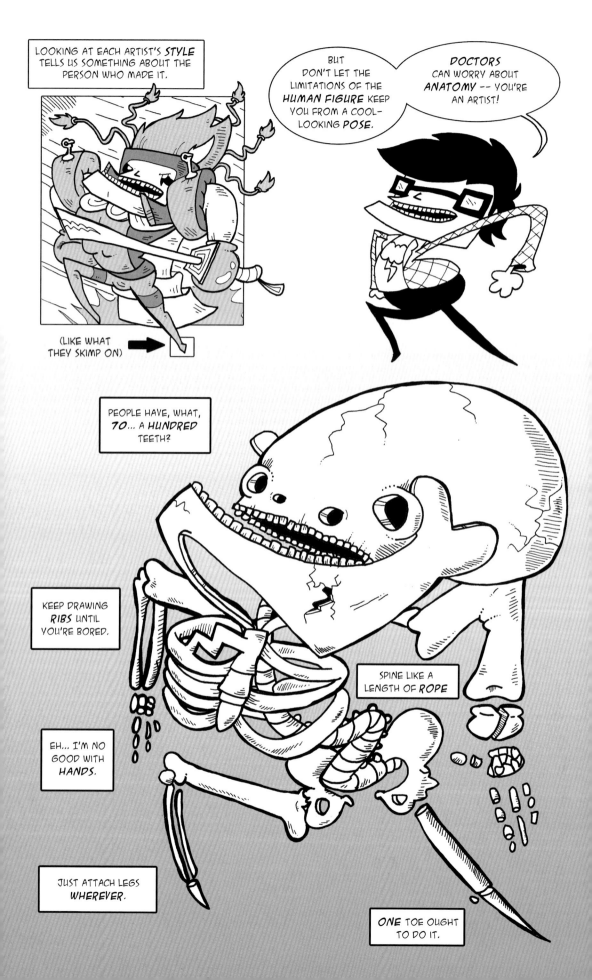

ART RANGES FROM *REALISTIC* TO *REPRESENTATIONAL* TO REALLY -- I MEAN REALLY -- PHONING IT IN.

I, JUST... NOT EVEN *EYES*?

THERE ARE *SO MANY* STYLES, WHO CAN EVEN SAY WHAT'S *GOOD* ANYMORE?

IF YOU CAN KEEP READERS *EXCITED*, YOUR DRAWING SKILL MAY NOT EVEN *MATTER*.

CRAFT A REALLY GREAT *STORY* AND COMPELLING *CHARACTERS* AND NO ONE'S GOING TO CARE THAT YOU CAN'T DRAW FEET!

OR FACES OR HAIR OR SWORDS OR WOMEN OR HANDS OR GUNS OR SHADOWS...

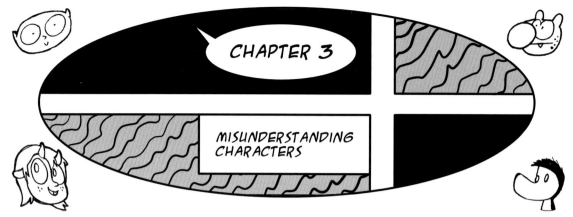

CHAPTER 3

MISUNDERSTANDING CHARACTERS

HOW DO YOU CREATE A COMPELLING CHARACTER -- AND DO YOU NEED TO?

Y'SEE, THE *SIMPLER* YOUR CHARACTERS ARE, THE MORE YOUR READERS CAN *IDENTIFY WITH* THEM.

DON'T WRITE A *COMPLEX* CHARACTER! THEY MAY ONLY BE RELATABLE TO A VERY SMALL AUDIENCE -- IF YOUR READERS *UNDERSTAND* THEM AT ALL!

HA! WE'VE ALL BEEN *THERE!*

INSTEAD, STICK TO A *SINGLE,* ABIDING THEME --

ONE *DIMENSION,* IF YOU WILL.

TAKE *ME,* FOR EXAMPLE -- I'M JUST A SNARKY *SMART-ASS.*

YOU DIDN'T PICK THIS UP TO HEAR MY REGRETS ABOUT NOT BEING *CLOSER* TO MY *PARENTS,* OR THAT I'M AFRAID TO ASK MY GIRLFRIEND TO *MOVE IN* BECAUSE I THINK SHE WILL SAY NO.

HEY, LOOK-- MORE *DUMB* COMICS!

COMICS SAY A LOT ABOUT THE PEOPLE WHO **READ** THEM!

HEROES DON'T HAVE TO BE **HEROIC** IN ANY TRADITIONAL SENSE -- JUST SOMEONE YOUR READERS CAN RELATE TO.

KIDS READ COMICS BECAUSE SUPERHEROES APPEAL TO THEIR NAÏVE SENSE OF **WONDER** AND **ADVENTURE**!

POW!

AS THEY MATURE AND HAVE NEW FEELINGS **DOWN THERE**, **TWEENS** SEEK OUT NEW CHARACTERS TO RELATE TO.

STAY **BACK**, RAVEN-HAIRED ENCHANTRESS! NONE MAY SEE MY MANLY **TEARS**!

That **UNICORN BITE** REQUIRES HEALING SALVE, YOU BRASHLY IMPULSIVE WARRIOR!

BEFORE THEY BECOME JADED, WORLD-WEARY **TEENS**, WITH HEROES TO MATCH.

BABES AND **BOMBS** AND **EXPLOSIONS** AND **SHOUTING** AND **FIST-FIGHTS** AND **SWORDS** AND DOUBLE-SQUARE-BARRELED LASER **GUNS**!

BIFF!

PRIMING READERS FOR CHARACTERS JUST AS DISAFFECTED AND ALIENATED AS THEY **ARE**.

PFFT... YEAH, "HEROES".

WHO THEN RETREAT INTO ONE LAST **GASP** OF THEIR **YOUTH**...

YOU SHOULD TRY LEARNING TO MAKE FRIENDS.

BEFORE THEY SUCCUMB TO THE JOYLESS **ROUTINE** THAT IS **ADULTHOOD**.

HOW DO CATS TYPE WITH SUCH LITTLE PAWS?

☐ YOUR MOM WANTS GRANDKIDS
☐ CHOCOLATE TASTES GOOD
☐ MENOPAUSE

I USE THE **MOUSE**.

SET IN THEIR WAYS, THEY LOOK FOR **NARRATORS** WHO TELL THEM WHAT THEY ALREADY **BELIEVE**.

I'VE GOT A LIST OF **57** CARD-CARRYING **GAY TERRORIST COMMUNIST HIPPIE WITCHES** IN THE FEDERAL GOVERNMENT TODAY,*

WOTTA SCOOP!

*SOURCE: DREDGE REPORT

BUT NOT YOU -- I'M SURE YOU'RE TOTALLY UNIQUE.

BUT WHAT ABOUT **VILLAINS?**

WHAT MAKES VILLAINS **TICK?**

YOUR **PERSONALITY TEST** SAYS YOU'RE A **DESTROYING, PROVOKING, UNFEELING, JUDGING** TYPE.

HAVE YOU CONSIDERED A CAREER IN A CALL CENTER?

VILLAINS CAN HAVE ANY NUMBER OF MOTIVES — THEY WERE **PICKED ON,** THEY WERE **OUTCASTS,** BLAH BLAH BLAH...

UH OH, BETTER BRING BACK THE **CALORIE** BURNING TYMES!

HA HA KRISTY YOU ARE SO MEAN

JUST DON'T MAKE THEM **TOO** RELATABLE-- THAT'S WHEN THINGS START TO GET **COMPLICATED.**

SIGN THIS **PETITION** TO OPPOSE THE MUTANT REGISTRATION ACT?

PLEASE?

IT CAN BE **SCARY** AND **CHALLENGING** FOR YOUR READERS IF YOU MAKE THEM **STOP** AND CONSIDER **WHY** VILLAINS ARE THE WAY THEY ARE.

SO MAKE YOUR VILLAINS SIMPLISTIC, MONSTROUS, AND ABOVE ALL -- **OBVIOUS!**

ROWR!?

KICK!

OH, THAT *REMINDS* ME! I ALMOST FORGOT ABOUT HOW TO WRITE *WOMEN!*

COUGH

ONE PAGE OUGHTA DO IT.

DESPITE NO COMIC BOOK READER EVER HAVING *SPOKEN* TO A WOMAN -- IT TURNS OUT THEY'RE A LOT LIKE *PEOPLE.*

THERE'S A WHOLE *RANGE* OF CHARACTERS WOMEN CAN PORTRAY!

SO ARE YOU SOMEONE'S *DAUGHTER* OR JUST A *PROSTITUTE?*

GIVE THEM *HOPES*, ASPIRATIONS, *MORALS* AND VICES LIKE YOU WOULD A *MALE* CHARACTER.

BUT THEREIN LIES THE *PROBLEM* -- YOU JUST WROTE ANOTHER *MAN!*

INSTEAD USE ANY ONE OF THE *MANY* CHARACTER MOTIVATIONS THAT ARE *UNIQUE* TO WOMEN.

HMM... WHAT IN THEIR *PAST* WOULD MOST AFFECT A FEMALE CHARACTER?

1. RAPE
2. RAPE
3. RAPE
4. RAPE
5. RAPE
6. RAPE
7. RAPE
8. RAPE

BUT THAT'S THE PARADOX OF TRYING TO WRITE *"WOMEN"* --

THERE'S NO *ONE* KIND OF *"WOMAN"* ANY MORE THAN THERE IS ANY ONE KIND OF *MAN.*

HMM...MAYBE I'M *OVER-THINKING* IT. MAYBE WE JUST NEED SOMETHING PRETTY TO LOOK AT.

LIKE A SEXY *LAMP.*

YOU MAY HAVE NOTICED I HAVEN'T MENTIONED *PEOPLE OF COLOR.*

THAT'S *RIGHT!* I *HAVEN'T!*

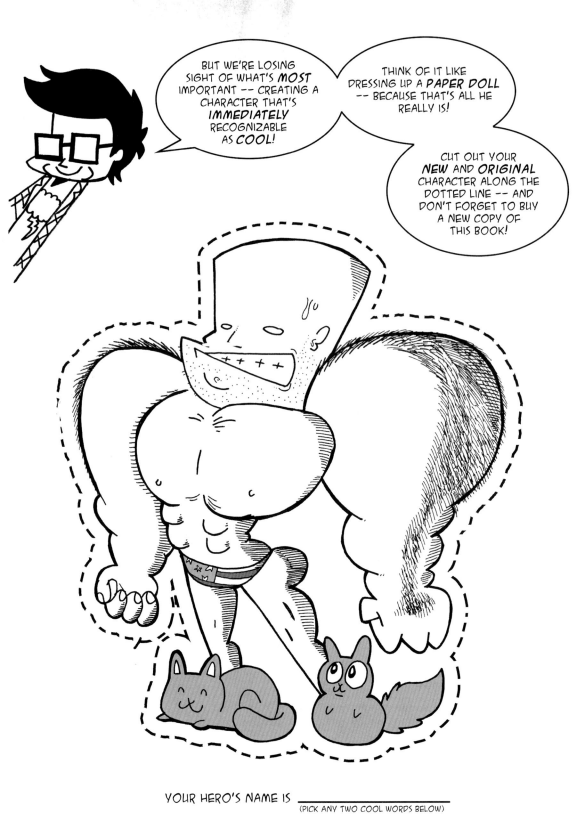

AWESOME BADASS ACCESSORIES

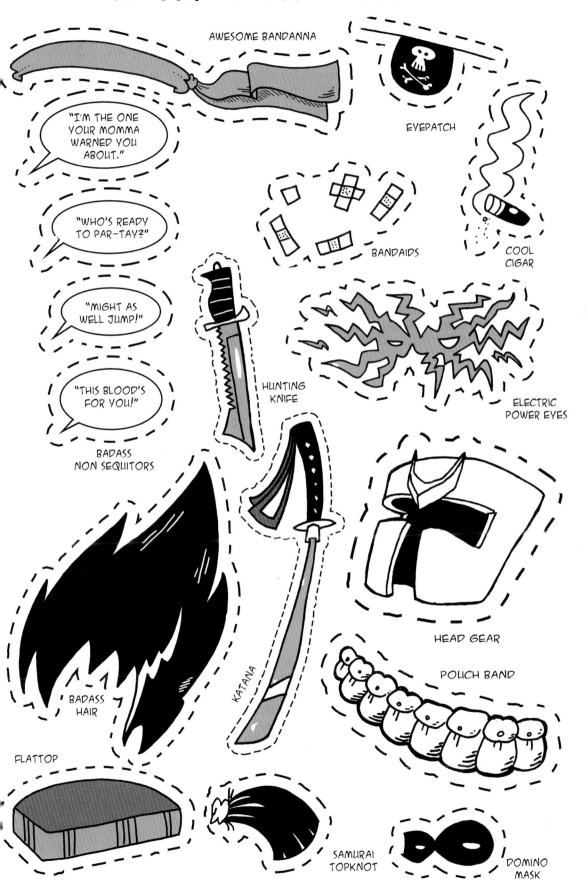

YOU CAN'T USE THE SAME **BADASS** WORDS TO NAME YOUR HEROINE! HER NAME'S GOTTA BE **SEXY!** SOME COMBINATION OF...

LADY	ASS	WONDER	ANGEL	MISTRESS	GIRL
NIGHT	WIDOW	FIRE	STORM	FANTASIA	BUNNY
POWER	DEATH	BOMB	BABE	HIT	TITS MCGEE

*FOR MORE IDEAS, CONSULT YOUR LOCAL STRIPPER!

SEXY BADASS ACCESSORIES

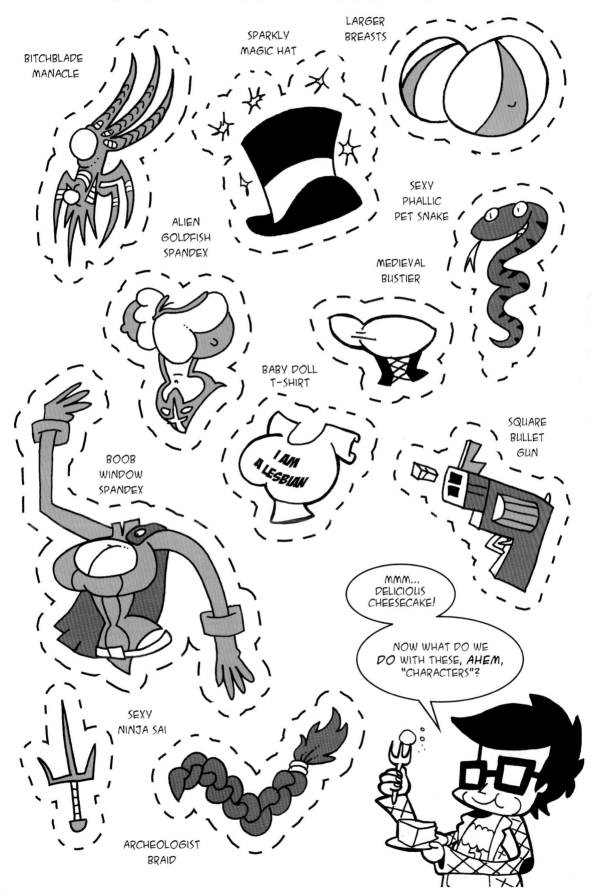

CHAPTER 4

STORYTELLING

-BLAMMO!

...OR WAS IT *START* WITH A BANG?

SOME ANCIENT CULTURES BELIEVED *TIME* WAS *CYCLICAL*.

RATHER THAN START FROM *NOTHING*, THEY TAKE SOMETHING *OLD* AND MAKE IT *NEW* AGAIN.

THE MOST ENDURING STORIES *SURVIVE* BECAUSE THEY ARE ALWAYS *REINVENTING* THEMSELVES.

COMIC BOOKS ARE NO DIFFERENT -- THEY EXPLOIT THE *SAME* IDEAS *TIME* AND *TIME* AGAIN!

TICK
TICK
TICK

12
9   3
6

Panel 1:

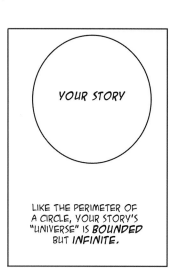

YOUR STORY

LIKE THE PERIMETER OF A CIRCLE, YOUR STORY'S "UNIVERSE" IS *BOUNDED* BUT *INFINITE.*

Panel 2:

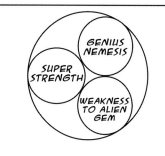

GENIUS NEMESIS

SUPER STRENGTH

WEAKNESS TO ALIEN GEM

THE *FIRST* ELEMENTS YOU PLACE INSIDE THAT UNIVERSE TAKE UP THE *GREATEST* AREA.

THEY'RE THE *FOUNDATION* THAT *DEFINE* THE CHARACTER AND THE WORLD OF YOUR STORY.

Panel 3:

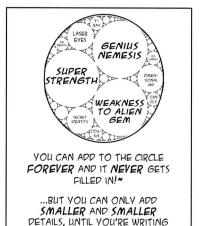

Y-RAY, LASER EYES, ICE BREATH, GENIUS NEMESIS, HOT VISION, SUPER STRENGTH, DIMEN-SIONAL IMP, CAN FLY, WEAKNESS TO ALIEN GEM, SECRET IDENTITY, COU-SIN

YOU CAN ADD TO THE CIRCLE *FOREVER* AND IT *NEVER* GETS FILLED IN!*

...BUT YOU CAN ONLY ADD *SMALLER* AND *SMALLER* DETAILS, UNTIL YOU'RE WRITING STORIES ABOUT THE HERO'S *DOG.*

*YOU'VE MADE AN APOLLONIAN GASKET. IMPRESS YOUR FRIENDS!

Panel 4:

ANOTHER RECURSIVE SHAPE IS THE *SIERPINSKI TRIANGLE.*

CAN YOU THINK OF ANY POPULAR *FRANCHISE** THAT RE-USES THE *SAME BASIC STORY,* ONLY ADDING IN PROGRESSIVELY *SMALLER* DETAILS?

*OKAY IT'S A VIDEO GAME AND NOT A COMIC. STAY WITH ME.

Panel 5:

UNFORTUNATELY, IF YOU KEEP THIS UP, YOU'LL RUN INTO A PROBLEM OF *CONTINUITY.*

THERE WILL BE SO MANY THINGS GOING ON -- AND IN SO MANY PLACES -- HOW DO YOU KEEP IT ALL STRAIGHT? WHICH ONE IS THE *REAL* STORY?

HEY, I ONLY *WORK* HERE.

Panel 6:

TRICK QUESTION!

THEY'RE *ALL* THE REAL STORY!

Panel 7:

THIS CREATES A PARADOX CALLED *SCHRÖDINGER'S CATWOMAN,* WHERE MULTIPLE CONTINUITIES CAN CO-EXIST WITHOUT CONTRADICTING ONE ANOTHER.

Panel 8:

AND MAYBE SOME OF THE STORIES ARE COMPLETE GARBAGE, BUT LIKE A *HOARDER* WITH HIS TRASH, THEY'RE ALL KEPT *--IN CONTINUITY!*

THESE *COUNTLESS* STORIES, CHARACTERS, AND PLOTS THAT YOUR READERS HAVE BEEN FOLLOWING *RELIGIOUSLY* HAVE BUILT UP A NICE LITTLE *FRANCHISE!*

AND YOU KEEP *ADDING* TO IT UNTIL...

WHOA!

...IT *COLLAPSES* UNDER ITS OWN *WEIGHT!*

WHUMP

SO WHAT DO YOU DO WHEN THIS *HOUSE OF CARDS* COLLAPSES?

YOU START OVER!

THERE'S ONE LAST DETAIL I FORGOT TO MENTION...

...DEATH!

THIS MAY COME AS A **SHOCK,**

SWIK!

OOPS.

NECK SNAP!

AND I DON'T WANT TO **BEAT** YOU OVER THE **HEAD** WITH IT

HA! HAHAHAHA

KLONK

BUT SUPERHEROES MEET THEIR **MAKER** PRETTY **OFTEN.**

AW, NERTZ.

AND WHILE IT **SEEMS** LIKE **THE END**

NO ONE **STAYS DEAD** FOR VERY LONG.

BUT IF YOU KILL OFF, BRING BACK, AND KILL OFF, AND BRING BACK YOUR CHARACTERS...

EVENTUALLY EVEN **DEATH** LOSES ITS IMPACT.

LAZARUS PIT
1 NO LIFE GUARD ON DUTY
2 WE DON'T SWIM IN YOUR TOILET; DON'T PEE IN...

3 FT.

AND IT ALL BECOMES A BIG **JOKE!**

CHAPTER 5

WEBCOMICS &
SELF-PUBLISHING

LET'S SAY YOU'VE GOT A VISION FOR A COMIC THAT'S JUST TOO GOOD TO BE CONFINED TO PAPER!

THEN YOU NEED A MEDIUM WITH NO MEDDLING SUITS, NO PESKY EDITORS, AND NO BARRIERS TO ENTRY.

YOU NEED WEBCOMICS!

MAYBE YOU HAVE A REVOLUTIONARY METAPHOR THAT LAYS BARE THE TRAGIC WAGES OF PREJUDICE...

...OR A NEVER-BEFORE-DONE TAKE ON HOW RELIGION IS ILLOGICAL...

...OR MAYBE YOU'RE A BRO MAKING A DEATH-BED CONVERSION TO SECOND-WAVE FEMINISM...

I AM A DOG BUT DON'T IGNORE MY SENTIENCE! PLEASE GIVE ME SOME HUMAN COFFEE!

HERE IS SOME TOILET WATER, A DRINK FOR DOGS!

Σ NEW! DRINK
SONIC CHAI ESP
RASPBERRY RAIN
OBAMA BLAST
$ $12.5

EVERYTHING IS AN ABOMINATION! I HATE FUN!

EXTRA JUDGMENTAL BIBLE

HEY, STOP PATRIARCHING YOUR PRIVILEGE IN MY LIVED EXPERIENCE!

ALLOW ME TO CLOSE WITH A PASSAGE FROM THIS VALERIE SOLANAS MANIFESTO.

WHEN YOU PUBLISH YOURSELF, YOU'RE FREE TO EXERCISE YOUR BOUNDLESS IMAGINATION!

BUY THIS PRINT

WHY PIZZA IS BETTER THAN BEING MAULED TO DEATH BY BEARS

1 PIZZA TASTES GOOD

BUY
BUY
BUY
BUY
BUY
BUY
BUY
BUY

BUY → BUY →

BUY THIS AS A PRINT RIGHT NOW!!

YOU CAN PRINT UP **ANYTHING** YOU LIKE -- WITH NO FILTER!

LOOSE CHANGE: THE GRAPHIC NOVEL

GOD HATES SHIRTS

GOD HATES SIGNS

...WHETHER IT'S A GOOD IDEA OR NOT!

SO CALL UP JUNO, FIRE UP YOUR MODEM, AND REGISTER YOURSELF A SITE AT GEOCITIES! BECAUSE IT'S TIME TO JOIN THE WEB 1.5 REVOLUTION!

BECAUSE NOW **ANYONE** CAN MAKE A COMIC!

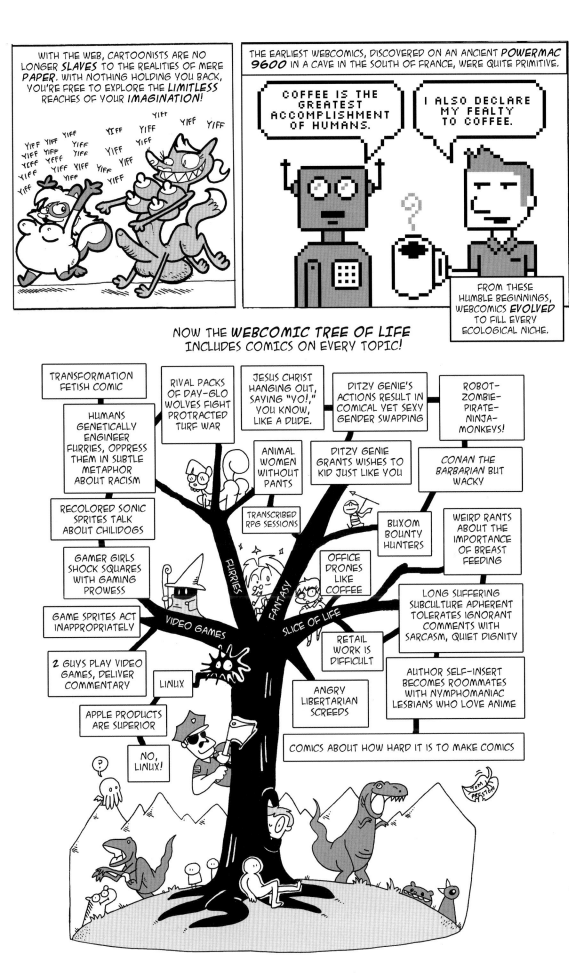

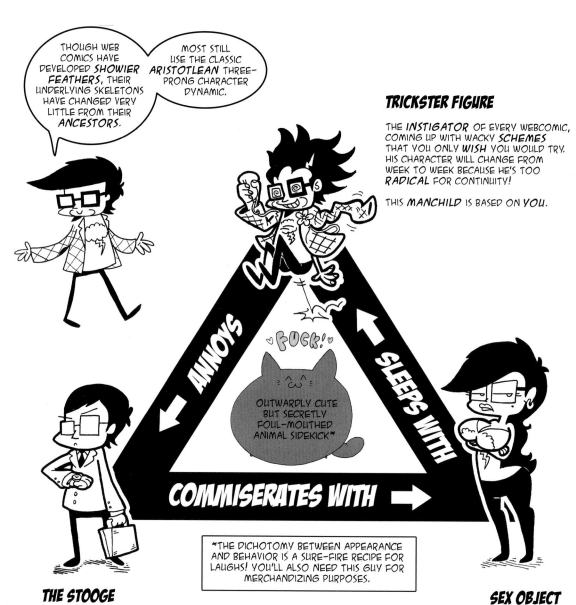
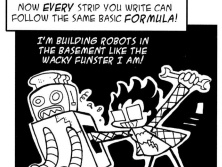

THE **FEMALE** CHARACTER SHOULD BE ESPECIALLY CRABBY AND HUMORLESS TO CONTRAST WITH THE WACKY MANCHILD.

THIS IS CALLED A **FOIL**.

USE HER TO ESTABLISH YOUR HERO'S CRED AS A **POLITICALLY-INCORRECT** REBEL BY DISRESPECTING HER.

YOUR COMMENTS ARE INAPPROPRIATE AND I WON'T SLEEP WITH YOU NO MATTER HOW MANY STAR WARS ANALOGIES YOU MAKE ABOUT MY BREASTS.

THEN YOU AND THE DEATH STARS ARE **FIRED**.

OR FLIP THE SCRIPT AND WRITE THE WOMAN AS A **SEXUALLY AGGRESSIVE LESBIAN**. THIS DEMONSTRATES THAT YOUR COMIC IS INCLUSIVE OF SEXUAL MINORITIES BUT WITHOUT HAVING TO SHOW ALL THAT GROSS GAY STUFF.

(PLUS IT DOESN'T COUNT AS RAPE IF IT'S A GIRL DOING IT!)

OH NERTS

SHE CAN ALSO BE ASIAN, BECAUSE ASIANS ARE HOT. REMEMBER, ALL ASIANS COME FROM JAPAN, WEAR SAILOR FUKUS, SPEAK IN PIDGIN ENGLISH, AND LOVE AMERICAN MANBOYS.*

YOU WATCH NARUTO? I LOVE NARUTO!

❋ SEE CHAPTER 6

NOW THAT YOU'VE GOT YOUR **CHARACTERS**, YOU NEED A **THEME** FOR YOUR COMIC.

IF THE CHARACTERS ARE YOUR **BONES**, THINK OF THE **THEME** AS THE FANCY SKIN TO DISTRACT READERS FROM THE FACT THAT YOUR COMIC DOESN'T HAVE ANY **FLESH**.

BUT PRODUCING NEW, ORIGINAL STORIES MEANS **RISK** THAT COULD SCARE AWAY YOUR AUDIENCE!

WHEN IT'S MUCH **EASIER** TO MAKE YOUR COMIC ABOUT THINGS MOST PEOPLE ARE ALREADY FAMILIAR WITH.

HEY GROK, HOW MUCH DO YOU LOVE GOLF?

I LOVE PLAYING GOLF

ALMOST AS MUCH AS I LOVE THE SACRIFICE OF OUR LORD AND SAVIOR JESUS CHRIST

FOR A WEBCOMIC, THAT MIGHT BE A STORY ABOUT VIDEO GAMES...

...OR VIDEO GAMES...

...OR **VIDEO GAMES!**

FOR MAXIMUM *GEEK CRED,* YOUR WEBCOMIC NEEDS A *SHIBBOLETH.*

A SHIBBOLETH IS A SECRET *CODE WORD* KNOWN ONLY TO MEMBERS OF A CERTAIN GROUP -- IT'S A QUICK WAY TO IDENTIFY LIKE-MINDED PEOPLE!

IF YOU'RE WITH PEOPLE WHO *ALSO* RECOGNIZE THE SHIBBOLETH, THEN YOU KNOW YOU'RE AMONG *FRIENDS.*

TO POP-CULTURE *GEEKS,* IT'S AN INSIDE JOKE *AND* A WAY TO FEEL *SUPERIOR* TO THOSE WHO DON'T GET THE SAME REFERENCES AS YOU!

CAPTAIN *SOLO* OF THE *GALACTICA,* LET'S RIDE *FALCOR* TO *HYRULE* TO FIGHT THE *SITH* LORD OF *MORIA!*

NERDS ARE ETERNALLY ENGAGED IN THE DICK-WAVING CONTEST THAT IS ESTABLISHING *GEEK CRED.* OBSESSION WITH SOME POP CULTURE EPHEMERA IS A BADGE OF HONOR -- PROOF THAT THEY ARE "GEEKIER THAN THOU".

A BIG PART OF WEBCOMIC HUMOR IS *"BEING RANDOM",* WHICH INVOLVES REPEATING A FEW SPECIFIC KEY TOPICS DETERMINED BY POPULAR CONSENSUS TO BE RANDOM, INCLUDING:

- **ZOMBIES**
- **NINJAS**
- **PIRATES**
- **MONKEYS**
- **ROBOTS**
- **ABRAHAM LINCOLN**
- **UNICORNS**
- **NAZIS**

NIKOLA TESLA!

MENTION TESLA WHENEVER YOU CAN -- NERDS LOVE TESLA BECAUSE HE WAS A SCIENTIST AND WAS BULLIED BY THOMAS EDISON WHO PROBABLY ALSO MADE HIM DO HIS HOMEWORK FOR HIM.

MANY NERDS IMAGINE THEMSELVES AS FRUSTRATED INTELLECTUALS WHO ARE UNAPPRECIATED BY SOCIETY, AND TESLA'S STORY PROVIDES AN EASY EXPLANATION FOR THEIR OWN UNDISCOVERED GENIUS.

ONCE YOU'VE DEFINED THE TRIBAL IN-GROUP, YOU CAN HELP MAINTAIN INTERNAL COHESION OF THE FAN GROUP BY TURNING THEIR ATTENTION AGAINST A COMMON ENEMY.

THERE ARE PLENTY OF INDEFENSIBLE PARIAHS TO CHOOSE FROM -- BUT HERE ARE A FEW FAVORITES:

FUNDAMENTALISTS

HIPSTERS

THE GUY WHO CANCELED FIREFLY

JACK THOMPSON

THE 3 STAGES OF A WEB COMIC

NOW YOU'RE READY TO **DEBUT** YOUR WEB COMIC!

ON THE WEB, YOU COULD DRAG A STORY ON FOR **DECADES** WITHOUT ANY RESOLUTION IF YOU WANTED TO, BUT YOUR TYPICAL WEB COMIC HAS **3** STAGES.

FOLLOW THIS PATH TO INTERNET **FAME!**

START

STALL BY HAVING YOUR CHARACTERS INTRODUCE THEMSELVES!

OUR ONLY THOUGHT IS TO ENTERTAIN YOU.

FEED ME.

THAT'S **ONE** WEEK DOWN!

USE UP THE ONE **JOKE** THAT MADE YOU WANT TO START IN THE FIRST PLACE.

MATH MATH MATH MATH

BY THE THIRD STRIP, YOUR CHARACTERS **YELL** AT YOU FOR NOT DRAWING WELL ENOUGH. THIS IS CALLED **BREAKING THE FOURTH WALL** AND IS TOTALLY ORIGINAL.

WHO ARE YOU TALKING TO?

YOU SUCK

STAGE 1 — THE COMIC STARTS AS A LIGHT-HEARTED **GAG STRIP**, LIKE THE SUNDAY FUNNIES -- ONLY TARGETING HIP YOUNG **INTERNET** USERS INSTEAD OF HIP **OLD** GOLF ENTHUSIASTS.

ASK ARTISTS TO DONATE **FAN ART** TO FILL SPACE WHILE YOU COWER UNDER YOUR BED.

FEMALE CHARACTER YELLS AT YOU FOR DRAWING HER **BREASTS TOO BIG**

--TURNING HORNY OGLING INTO **IRONIC COMMENTARY.**

FIVE STRIPS IN AND YOU **STILL** DON'T HAVE A **CONVENTION** NAMED AFTER YOU!

PAY ATTENTION TO ME!

LINK'S HAIR IS **BROWN!**

THREATEN TO **QUIT** UNLESS YOU GET MORE COMMENTS AND/OR FACEBOOK **LIKES.**

START INSERTING YOUR **FETISHES** INTO THE COMIC.

FROGMOUTH LESBIANSSSSS

GIVE UP ON ALL THE THINGS!

APOLOGIZE FOR NOT UPDATING, THEN TAKE A **YEAR-LONG HIATUS.**

SHADOWY FIGURES **MENACE** YOUR WACKY CENTRAL CHARACTERS.

STAGE 2 — THE **MISKATONIC GAMBIT** -- MARKED BY THE FIRST REFERENCE TO THE ELDER GOD **CTHULHU**, THE COMIC BECOMES DARKER AND STRANGER AS YOU STEAL IDEAS FROM MORE NOTABLE ARTISTS.

R'LYEH, PLEASE

GUMDROP SHORTCUT

DOES YOUR **MISCARRIAGE** MEAN WE'RE GOING TO MISS OUR **RAID** TONIGHT?

YOU CROSS A LINE AND CAUSE AN INTERNET **SHITSTORM**

PHALLUS LUPUS

DEFLECT CRITICISM BY STARTING A **CHARITY**

DONATE YOUR FANS' **MONEY**, BUT KEEP THE **PRAISE** FOR YOURSELF!

FINISH

YOU'VE **PROVEN** YOUR WEB COMIC CHOPS! TIME TO TRANSITION TO A TRULY **PROFESSIONAL** MEDIUM...

...LIKE PUPPETS!

STAGE 3 — YOUR COMIC STRIP TRIES TO GROW MORE 'ADULT' -- INTRODUCING SUBPLOTS, DEATHS, AND CRIBBING PLOTS FROM **ANIME.**

NOW THAT YOU HAVE THE INTERNET'S **FULL ATTENTION**, YOU PUT YOUR **FOOT** IN YOUR MOUTH.

BUT THE REAL EXCITEMENT OF WEBCOMICS IS THAT YOU DON'T NEED TO WAIT FOR A RESPONSE; YOUR AUDIENCE CAN GIVE YOU INSTANTANEOUS FEEDBACK AS SOON AS YOU POST YOUR COMIC!

YOU SUCK!

WHAT!? HOW DARE YOU CRITICIZE ME, INTERNET PERSON!

YOU CAN'T CRITICIZE THIS ENTERTAINMENT BECAUSE (PICK ONE)

A. YOU'RE GETTING IT FOR FREE!

B. I'D LIKE TO SEE YOU DO BETTER, YOU TALENTLESS NOBODY!

C. I'VE HAD 20 VISITORS TO MY WEBSITE TODAY, SO OBVIOUSLY MY COMIC IS GREAT!

LET THOSE NOOBS ON TEH INTERWEBS HAVE THEIR WEB COMICS, CHASING BRAIN-DEAD CORPORATE CULTURE -- I'M GOING OFF THE GRID.

THE ONLY REAL COMICS ARE THE ONES YOU MAKE YOURSELF.

YOU PROBABLY HAVEN'T HEARD OF IT.

IT'S KIND OF A BIG DEAL--

SELF-PUBLISHING!

DID I MENTION I DON'T EVEN OWN A TV?

TAKE ON THE BIG TWO BY DOING ALL THE WORK YOURSELF -- SELLING YOUR OWN COMIC ONE ISSUE AT A TIME!

HOW HARD COULD IT BE? YOU'RE ONLY COMPETING WITH EVERY OTHER INDEPENDENT ARTIST.

YOU COULD MAKE LITERALLY DOLLARS!

YOU WON'T BE A POOR, ANONYMOUS COMIC CREATOR WORKING IN SOME SWEATSHOP -- YOU GET TO BE YOUR OWN BOSS!

WORKING IN YOUR OWN SWEATSHOP!

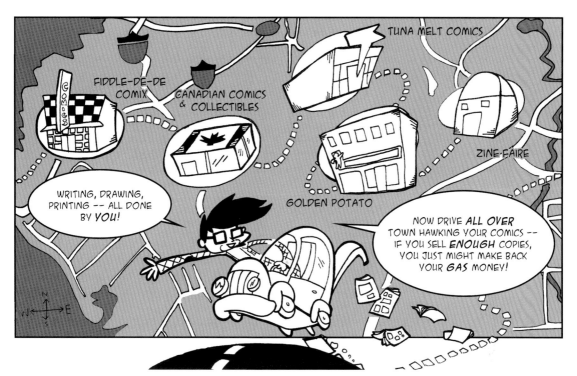

JAPANESE COMIC ART WAS VERY *CARTOON-LIKE*, INFLUENCED BY WESTERN ARTISTS SUCH AS WALT DISNEY AND WINDSOR MCKAY.

"ASTRO BOY" BY OSAMU TEZUKA, THE *"GOD OF COMICS"*

BUT THAT CHANGED IN THE MID-20TH CENTURY WHEN ANIMATORS LIKE *MIYAZAKI*...

GOOD CATBUS!

PURRR

...AND GRAPHIC NOVELS LIKE OTOMO'S *AKIRA* SHAPED MANGA INTO WHAT IT IS TODAY.

GOOD TETSUO!

AND IT'S BEEN *STUCK* THERE EVER *SINCE*.

PURRR

THERE'S MANGA FOR MEN AND WOMEN, YOUNG AND OLD, SO NO *SINGLE* DEFINITION FITS!

AND YET *SOMEHOW*...

IT ALL SEEMS KIND OF THE *SAME*!

MANGA

JAPAN IS A MODEL OF *EFFICIENCY*, AND THEIR COMICS ARE NO DIFFERENT.

SO WHAT MAKES FOR GOOD *MANGA*?

¥800

¥9500

FIND OUT WHAT WORKED FOR ARTISTS BEFORE -- AND *COPY* THEM!

AH, HERE IT IS!

HOW TO DRAW MANGA

TENTACLES

NOW, I'M not **SINGLING OUT** MANGA HERE...

BUT IT DOES HAVE ONE **PERVASIVE** STYLE THAT YOU MUST NOT **DEVIATE** FROM.

MANGA FANS HAVE A VERY **REFINED** -- OR **NARROW** -- TASTE IN ART.

UGH, WHAT A BEAST! WOULD NOT DO.

SO HERE ARE THE **RULES** TO FOLLOW:

HOW TO DRAW A MANGA FACE

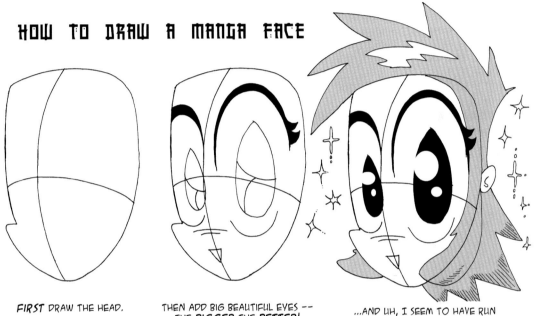

FIRST DRAW THE HEAD.

THEN ADD BIG BEAUTIFUL EYES -- THE **BIGGER** THE **BETTER!**

...AND UH, I SEEM TO HAVE RUN OUT OF **SPACE,** SO JUST DRAW A LITTLE **TRIANGLE** AND SOME **HASH LINES.**

IT'S HARD TO CONVEY EMOTION WITHOUT A **MOUTH** OR **NOSE,** BUT MANGA HAS ITS OWN **SHORT-HAND.** SO YOU DON'T HAVE TO ACTUALLY **DRAW** AN EXPRESSION!

NERVOUS!

ANGRY!

HORNY... OR MAYBE SLEEPING?

THERE YOU HAVE IT, THE **FULL RANGE** OF EMOTION!

INSANELY HAPPY!

SUICIDAL DEPRESSION!

AND IF NONE OF THOSE WORK -- JUST **WRITE IT OUT.**

ANGRY

ANATOMY OF A MANGA GIRL

USE THESE STYLISTIC FLOURISHES TO *TART UP* YOUR CHARACTERS
TO APPEAL TO THE DISCERNING TASTES OF *MANGA* READERS!

HAIR
THE HAIR SHOULD ALWAYS BE A COLOR NOT FOUND IN NATURE TO EMPHASIZE HER UNIQUENESS. BASE THE HAIRSTYLE ON YOUR FAVORITE *FLOCK OF SEAGULLS* MEMBER!

EYES
HETEROCHROMATIC EYES SHOW THAT YOUR CHARACTER IS A UNIQUE SOUL WHO STANDS APART FROM THE CROWD!

CHEEKS
YOU'LL NEED THESE BECAUSE THIS IS WHERE THE BLUSH GOES WHEN SOMETHING SEXY HAPPENS AND, BELIEVE ME, SOMETHING SEXY WILL HAPPEN A LOT.

BREASTS
BECAUSE JAPAN IS IN THE EASTERN HEMISPHERE, THE CORIOLIS EFFECT CAUSES EACH INDIVIDUAL BREAST TO BOUNCE OUT OF SEQUENCE.

LOLIGOTH CRINOLINE
A MANGA GIRL IS PRACTICALLY NAKED IF SHE'S NOT DRESSED LIKE AN 1890S CHILD PROSTITUTE.

CUDDLY AND MERCHANDISABLE ANIMAL SIDEKICK
EVERY MANGA GIRL NEEDS SOMETHING TO ENTICE PRETEENS TO BUY CELLPHONE DANGLES SO YOU'LL ALSO NEED TO KNOW

BY THE POWER OF LASAGNA, I WILL PUNISH MONDAYS!

EARS
CAT EARS INDICATE THAT A GIRL HAS DESIRABLE KITTEN-LIKE ATTRIBUTES LIKE A HAPPY BUBBLY PERSONALITY, BOUNDLESS ENERGY, AND TAPE-WORMS.

WHAT KIND OF MUTANTS DO YOU HANG OUT WITH?

CAT HANDS
LIKE A CAT, A GIRL HAS GIANT WEIRD CAT GLOVES.

TAIL
LIKE A CAT, A GIRL HAS A TAIL.

UNDERWEAR
VITALLY IMPORTANT!!!

PRO TIP: PAIR YOUR MANGA GIRL WITH AN INEFFECTUAL EVERYMAN WHOM YOUR AUDIENCE CAN RELATE TO!

HOW TO DRAW A MANGA ANIMAL

TIP: THE SECRET TO CUTE MANGA ANIMALS IS ELIMINATING AS MANY DETAILS AS POSSIBLE. WHO WOULD WANT TO PET THIS GROSS THING?

BETTER, BUT IS IT CUTE ENOUGH? THIS CAT STILL HAS JOINTS!

FINALLY, YOU'VE ACHIEVED TRUE MANGA CUTENESS!

CREATING YOUR MANGA CHARACTER

MAKE YOUR CHARACTERS **SEXY**, BECAUSE NO ONE WILL PAY ATTENTION IF THEY AREN'T **PRETTY** -- JUST LIKE IN REAL LIFE!

HEY... YOU'RE *CUTE!*

HEY... YOU'RE *CUTE!*

HEY... YOU'RE *CUTE.*

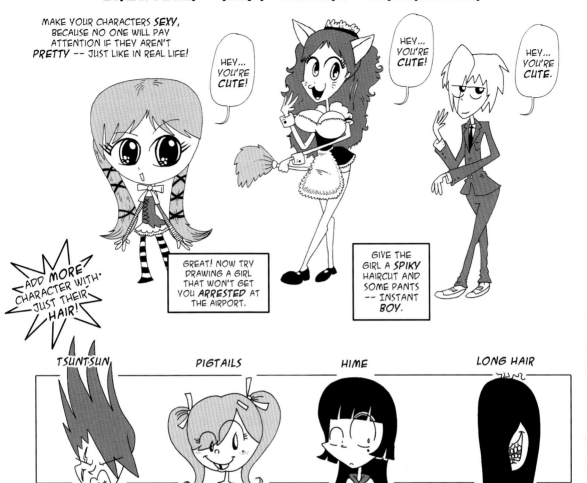

ADD MORE CHARACTER WITH JUST THEIR HAIR!

GREAT! NOW TRY DRAWING A GIRL THAT WON'T GET YOU **ARRESTED** AT THE AIRPORT.

GIVE THE GIRL A **SPIKY** HAIRCUT AND SOME PANTS -- INSTANT **BOY.**

TSUNTSUN

PIGTAILS

HIME

LONG HAIR

SPIKY HAIR INDICATES AN IMPULSIVE AND ENERGETIC CHARACTER WHO CAN BLAST LIGHTNING FROM HIS WRISTS CONTINUOUSLY FOR **26** PAGES.

PIGTAILS SHOW A CHARACTER IS CUTE AND INNOCENT -- OR OPERATES A TOTALLY LEGAL AND NOT AT ALL SKETCHY WEBCAM SHOW.

THE HIME EMBODIES THE TRADITIONAL JAPANESE VIRTUES OF DIGNITY, ELEGANCE, AND BEING THE BORING NON-SEXPOT THE HERO WILL EVENTUALLY MARRY IN THE FINAL CHAPTER.

LONG HAIR MEANS THAT A CHARACTER LIVES INSIDE YOUR TELEVISION.

HOW TO DRAW EVERYTHING ELSE

AND ALL OTHER OBJECTS GET FUN, FRIENDLY *SMILEY* FACES!

MOE PERSONIFICATION TURNS EVERYDAY THINGS INTO CUTE, LOVABLE PRETEEN GIRLS!

SORRY, MR. TAKAGI, IT APPEARS YOU HAVE **BRAIN** CANCER.

WHAT? I DON'T UNDERSTAND.

FO XLYI

I MEAN YOU HAVE THIS ADORABLE LITTLE GIRL ON YOUR BRAIN.

NYA!

AWW!

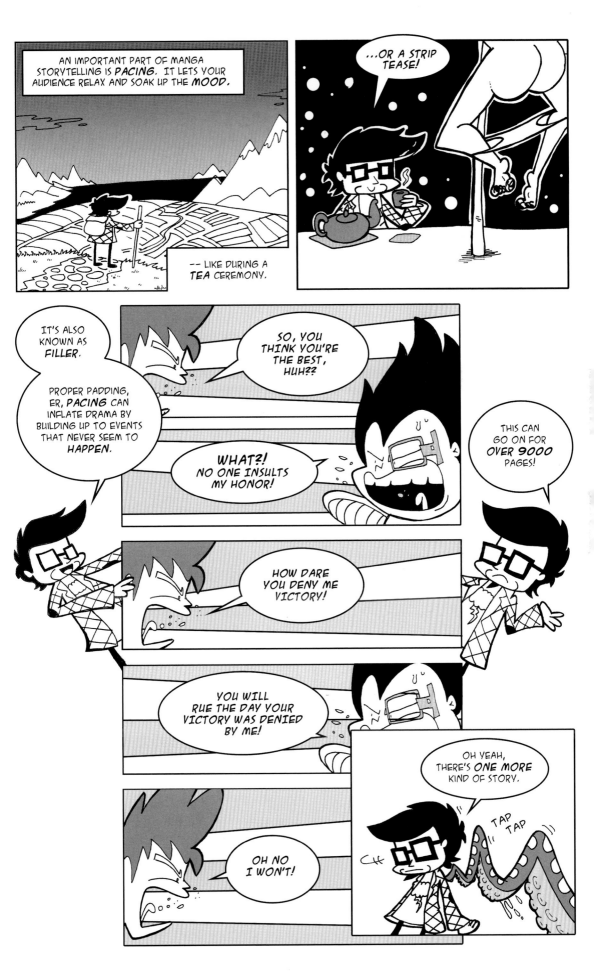

IN JAPAN, COMICS ARE READ BY **ADULTS!** THEY EVEN HAVE **ADULT THEMES**, ACHIEVING THE SAME LEVEL OF **RESPECT** AS...

...PORN.

50 SHADES OF GENJI

JAPAN HAS A LONG, PROUD

...THROBBING, SLIMY...

HISTORY OF **TENTACLES** IN EROTICA!

SLAM!

JOZ XYQK!

THE DREAM OF THE FISHERMAN'S WIFE
KATSUSHIKA HOKUSAI (1814)

BUT WHY SEX WITH **TENTACLES**?

NyYAAaHHH!!!

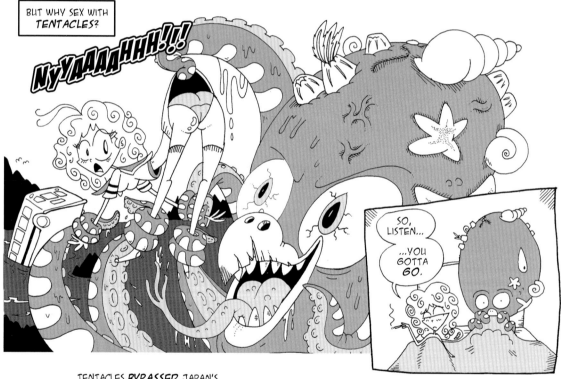

SO, LISTEN...

...YOU GOTTA **GO**.

TENTACLES **BYPASSED** JAPAN'S RIDICULOUSLY STRICT **CENSORSHIP** LAWS AGAINST SHOWING GENITALS.

BECAUSE COMICS OF **CONSENSUAL SEX** BETWEEN ADULTS WOULD JUST BE **WEIRD**.

THIS PURITANICAL ATTITUDE IS WHY MANGA HAS **CENSORED** ALL THE GOOD BITS ...KINDA.

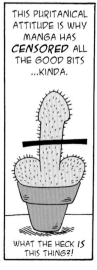

WHAT THE HECK **IS** THIS THING?!

WHAT COULD IT BE? DO I EAT IT? I'M SO **ALMOST** TURNED ON!

CAN THEY EVEN **SHOW** THIS?!

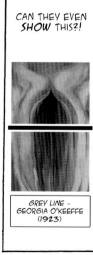

GREY LINE –
GEORGIA O'KEEFFE
(1923)

NOW YOU UNDERSTAND EVERYTHING THERE IS TO KNOW ABOUT *MANGA!*

TEEN MELODRAMA, GIANT ROBOTS AND *PANTY* SHOTS!

DON'T DO *DUMB* STUFF, LIKE...

GET IDEAS FROM YOUR COUNTRY'S STORIED *HISTORY!*

FOLLOW WORN *CLICHÉS* TO APPEAL TO FANS

BETTER *THAT* THAN WHEN YOU --

HMM... OR MAYBE I GOT THAT *BACKWARDS.*

STOP!

7

6 5 4

3 2 1

DON'T YOU KNOW HOW TO READ *MANGA?!*

BOTTOM TO *TOP,* RIGHT-TO-LEFT, DUMB GAIJIN!!

TRY SOMETHING *NEW!*

LIFE IS HELL

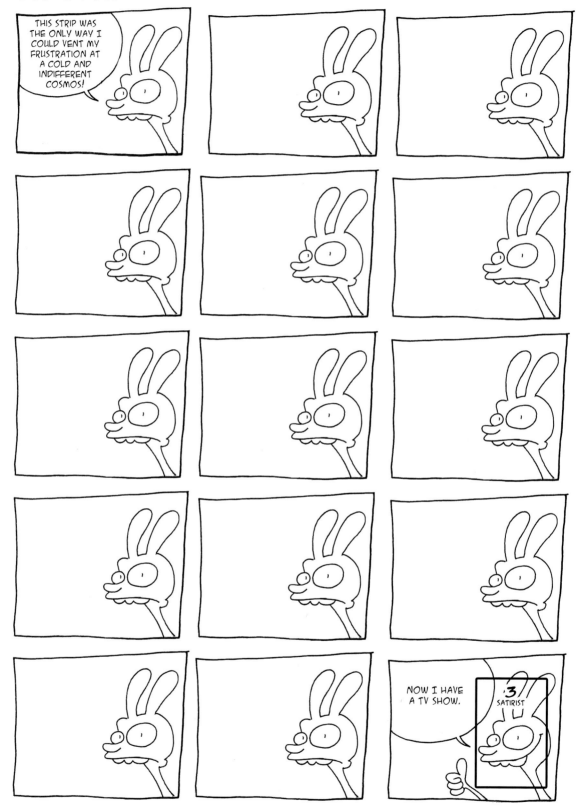

BUT STILL THERE IS A **MORE** LEARN'D INTELLECTUAL COMIC BOOK AUTHOR...

SUPREMEMAN CAN TOTALLY **BEAT UP** BETTER-MAN!

NO WAY!

WHAT DO THEY KNOW OF **HEROES?** THESE STORIES ARE **TRIFLES** NEXT TO THE DEEDS OF JEAN VALJEAN, OR LORD BYRON!

GETTING OVER HER PRIDE (AND **PREJUDICE!**) AGAINST COMICS AS A SERIOUS FORM OF LIT-TRA-CHURE, SHE MAKES SOME **SCRIBBLINGS** OF HER OWN.

MFA ENGLISH

WILDE CHILDE

THOUGH SHE KNOWS MORE OF **MELVILLE** THAN MAGNETO!

SWAG + SWAGGABILITY

WATCH ME NEG ON THIS CHICK

SHE LEARNS TO JUXTAPOSE THE LOWBROW AND HIGHBROW IN UNEXPECTED WAYS!

SEEMS LIKE WE'VE BEEN COMING TO THESE BALLS FOR YEARS

...I DIDN'T THINK THERE WERE ANY WOMEN HERE WHO WERE **STILL** UNMARRIED.

...THEN KINDA JUST KEEPS DOING THAT.

OHHHHHH MR.DARCY!

WINK

IT'S LIKE YOU'RE READING COMICS **AND** STUDYING!

Sweet Wuthering High

JAMES & JOYCE & ZOMBIES

Created by Kate Brontë

THE LITERARY DARLING SEEKS TO **REINVIGORATE** COMICS BY COMBINING 19TH CENTURY ENGLISH ROMANTIC FICTION AND SOMETHING **RANDOM** LIKE ZOMBIES OR WHATEVER ELSE IS POPULAR RIGHT NOW.

I'M TRYING TO MEET YOU **MOUTH-BREATHERS** HALFWAY!

4 LOWBROW SNOB

SIGNING TODAY!

SWEET WUTHERING HIGH

MEET KATE BRONTË

JAMES & JOYCE & ZOMBIE

SCI-FI

FANTASY

MYST

SHE'S MINING **HISTORY** FOR HER COMICS, BUT SHE ISN'T EXPLOITING HER **OWN** HISTORY.

ANOTHER ARTIST BELIEVES COMICS ARE *IMPORTANT* AND CAN ADDRESS HUMAN TRAGEDY WITHOUT *TRIVIALIZING* IT.

SO HE WRITES A COMIC BOOK ABOUT TERRIBLE THINGS HAPPENING TO *CARTOON MICE!*

5
MAUDLIN

HOW CAN I USE COMICS TO ADDRESS *SERIOUS* ISSUES?

THE KEY IS SUBTLE, UNDERSTATED METAPHOR!

HITLER
KATZ

SOON HE ACHIEVES THE TRUE MEASURE OF FAME: TED RALL GRUDGE-PISSING ON HIS GRAVE!

HE FINDS THIS APPROACH WORKS FOR *ALL SORTS* OF WEIGHTY SUBJECTS!

WHEW! MY DOGS ARE *BARKIN!*

行進！

BATAAN DEATH MARCH

GET MOVING, *SITTING BULL!*

I HAVE *RESERVATIONS* ABOUT THIS!

TRAIL OF TEARS

NOW HE HAS THE AUTHORITY TO TOSS OUT RAMBLINGS ON *ANY* TRAGEDY.

DESPITE ALL THE CRITICAL *ACCLAIM,* HE'LL NEVER BE ABLE TO SHAKE THE GUILT THAT HE'S PROFITING OFF HUMAN *TRAGEDY.*

WHY DID I SET ALL THOSE *GLUE TRAPS?*

I'M WORSE THAN *HITLER!*

BUT TO REACH EVEN HIGHER AS AN INTELLECTUAL COMIC AUTHOR, HE'D NEED A *PERSONALITY DISORDER...*

BEING AN INTELLECTUAL COMIC SUPERSTAR IS SOMETHING YOU'RE JUST **BORN** WITH...

...LIKE **ASPERGERS**.

I **FOCUSED** FOR YEARS **PERFECTING** MY STERILE COMIC STYLE.

THEY WERE LIKE **NOTHING** THE COMICS WORLD HAD EVER **SEEN**!

BUT **NO ONE** WAS INTERESTED! WHERE HAD I GONE **WRONG**?

MY PARENTS, TEACHERS, AND THERAPIST SAID I WAS EXCEPTIONAL! AM I JUST ... **AVERAGE**?

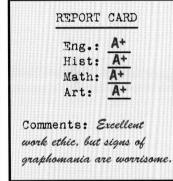

I DREW STORIES OF ANGST, DEFEAT, AND SELF-LOATHING IN **EQUILATERAL SQUARES**.

BUT THEN

AND SO

IMPERSONAL COMIC STRIPS OF SAD, **LONELY** PEOPLE BROUGHT ME CRITICAL **ACCLAIM**.

HOW-EVER

NONE OF IT MATTERS, FOR WE ARE BORN ASTRIDE THE **GRAVE**.

AFTER *REDEFINING* COMICS, YOU'VE MANAGED TO SHAKE OFF THE STINK OF THIS "FUNNY PAGES" RACKET, AND MADE IT TO THE *NE-PLUS-ULTRA* FOR EFFETE, SELF-HATING ARTISTS.

THE NEW YORKER

Nov. 1, 2004

A MAGAZINE WITH SUCH CLASSY JAPES AS...

But I **am** Pagliacchi!

You **had** to go north of 125th, didn't you?

IRONICALLY, THESE TASTEMAKERS WON'T LET YOU JOIN THE RANKS OF LEGITIMATE ARTISTS.

My **niece** also likes to draw.

BECAUSE COMICS -- WILL NEVER BE CONSIDERED *ART!*

DROWNING GIRL, ROY LICHTENSTEIN, 1963

CHAPTER 8

COMIC BOOK COLLECTORS AND FANBOYS

PEOPLE COLLECT ALL SORTS OF THINGS!

WHETHER IT'S COMIC BOOKS, TOYS, OR A LOCK OF HAIR FROM YOUR VICTIMS, THERE'S ALWAYS A MARKET FOR COLLECTIBLES!

FLEA MARKET

Sat-Sun
8am - 3pm

#1 GRANNY

RARE COMICS!!! $$$$$

RARE COMICS!!

AND JUST AS MANY WAYS TO WRING EVERY LAST CENT OUT OF COLLECTORS!

'EY, THIS IS A GREAT DEAL!

COMICS!!

RARE COMICS!!

#7 FACEPUNCH! THE MAN WHO PUNCHES FACES

Special ALL Letters to the Editor Issue!

SOME OF THESE COMICS ARE WORTH HUNDREDS!

I'LL SELL YOU THE WHOLE BOX FOR FIVE BUCKS.

IF SOMETHING IS PERCEIVED AS SCARCE OR VALUABLE, IT TRIGGERS AN UNCONTROLLABLE DESIRE TO CLUTCH IT TO ONE'S BOSOM!

IT'S AN IMPORTANT MECHANISM FOR SURVIVAL, PUSHING US TO COLLECT RESOURCES IN TIMES OF PLENTY TO PREPARE FOR THE FAMINE AHEAD.

YOU CAN SEE THE SAME BEHAVIOR IN PRIMITIVE ORGANISMS FROM PACKRATS...

...TO CARTOON DUCKS.

OCH!

THIS BEHAVIOR ISN'T *EXCLUSIVE* TO COMIC BOOKS...THERE HAVE ALWAYS BEEN *OBSESSIVE COLLECTORS*.

EGYPT, 1323 B.C.

WE'LL MAKE A FORTUNE SELLING THIS ON EGYPTBAY!

TURIN, ITALY, 1290

ONLY TEN FLORINS TO SEE THE SHROUD!

HOLLAND, 1637.

GOTTA CATCH ZE ALLEMAAL!

ONCE ENOUGH PEOPLE ASCRIBE VALUE TO SOMETHING THE URGE TO COLLECT IT SPREADS LIKE *MANIA*!

YOU'D BE A *FOOL* NOT TO GET A PIECE OF THAT!

24   24

CENT S

I'LL TELL YA WHY...

IF A FAN *OWNS* ENOUGH THINGS WITH THEIR FAVORITE CHARACTER *STAMPED* ON IT, THEY *BECOME* LIKE THAT WHICH THEY WORSHIP.

IT WORKED FOR *ED GEIN*, DIDN'T IT?

WHETHER IT'S A HARD-FOUGHT *TROPHY* OF THEIR VANQUISHED FOES...

LESS GRUESOME, BUT *NO EASIER* TO CLAIM.

CON EXCLUSIVE

OR TO GET IN TOUCH WITH THEIR GUIDING SPIRITS THROUGH OSMOSIS.

TO *BECOME* LIKE THOSE THEY *IDOLIZE*.

CONVENTION

FANS VALUE THE QUALITIES OR RICHES THEIR HEROES REPRESENT, AND WANT TO POSSESS THOSE TRAITS THEMSELVES.

THOG JONES COOKS HIS MEAT

AND IF THEY CAN'T HAVE THE REAL THING, A REPLICA WILL DO!

THE 12 LABORS OF THE TRVE FAN

ARGUING ON THE INTERNET

WAITING FOR THE THEATER TO OPEN

CONDESCENDING TO CHILDREN

FIGHTING FOR THE LATEST CONSOLE

DEFEATING CHARON AT MAGIC

KILLING A WHOLE SEASON OF SCRUBS

SORTING THE AUGEAN COMIC BOOK STACKS

CAMPING FOR RARE ITEMS

COLLECTING THE PROMOTIONAL CUPS

FINDING THE RARE BLIND BAG COLLECTIBLE

COSPLAYING AS THE CYCLOPS

HAGGLING WITH THE CENTAUR

BUT IT ISN'T JUST ABOUT *OWNING* THINGS. FANS LIKE TO BE PART OF SOMETHING *BIGGER* THAN THEMSELVES.

WELCOME TO THE 501ST LEGION. HERE'S YOUR OFFICIAL *UNIFORM*, THX-TRIPLE-ZERO!

MEETING OTHER FANS IS AN OPPORTUNITY TO *SOCIALIZE* AND SHARE THE THINGS YOU *ENJOY*.

BUT NAVIGATING THE *RULES* OF FANDOM CAN BE *TRICKY*.

VAMPIRE CON '99

YOU'LL FIND THEIR DIFFERENCES ARE *SUBTLE* BUT *IMPORTANT!*

RED AND YELLOW, A *MAGICAL* FELLOW.

PURPLE, RED, GREEN AND TAN, A *GALLIFREY* MAN!

EACH GROUP DEVELOPS ITS OWN CUSTOMS, ITS OWN *LANGUAGE*, INEXPLICABLE TO *OUTSIDERS*.

DARMOK... AND *JALAD*... AT *TANAGRA*...!

HODOR.

YOU CAN'T JUST *WALTZ UP* AND *BLEND IN* WITH THIS INSULAR GROUP.

HAI GUYZ!!!

VIDEO-GAMES ARE SO COOL, RIGHT?!

WHAT

HUH?

FANS ARE SO *GUARDED* BECAUSE, AS SOCIAL *OUTCASTS*, THIS CAMARADERIE IS A WELCOME CHANGE!

JOINING MEANS BEING PART OF A *SECRET* CLUB OF LIKE-MINDED PEOPLE WHO SHARE THE SAME *INTERESTS*, HOBBIES, JOKES -- ONE MIGHT EVEN SAY *CULTURE* AS YOU.

WHOOPS!

YOU'VE JOINED A *CULT!*

SERIES CANCELED!

AND EVERY CULT NEEDS *A LEADER!*

YOUR *CREATIONS* MAY BE THE ONLY *GLIMMER* OF LIGHT IN YOUR FANS' *SAD* EXISTENCE!

JOY DIVISION

CROW

THEY'RE ALREADY *PASSIONATE* ABOUT WHAT THEY LIKE, AND WILL BE *MORE* THAN HAPPY TO SPREAD YOUR GOSPEL!

HAVE YOU ACCEPTED *GRANT MORRISON* INTO YOUR LIFE?

AS A *CREATOR,* YOU CAN HARNESS THIS *DEDICATION* TO SHAPE THEIR VERY *LIVES!*

THOU SHALT *AIM TO MISBEHAVE.*

SQUEE!

JERUSALEM BROWNCOATS

WITH A GROUP OF LOYAL *FOLLOWERS,* YOU'LL DISCOVER SOMETHING MORE IMPORTANT THAN *MONEY.*

GREAT IDEA, BOSS!

HENCHMAN #3

HENCHMAN #2

HENCHMAN #1

POWER!

WHAT DID THE WOGGLE-BUG SAY?

BRING BACK FARSCAPE

TEAM EDWARD

I SHIP IT

LIVE LONG AND CARRY ON

FRIENDS IS MAGICAL

FREE HUGS

CHAPTER 9

CASHING OUT:
MAKING GOOD MONEY
WITH BAD IDEAS

LISTEN UP!

THIS IS A PROVEN, *CAN'T LOSE*, MONEY-MAKING STRATEGY THAT *WORKS*!!

IN COMICS, *FINE ART* ISN'T A REQUIREMENT, *CHARACTERS* CAN BE ONE-DIMENSIONAL, AND THE SAME STORIES ARE RECYCLED FOR *YEARS*!

TONIGHT ONLY
HOW TO MAKE $$$
in Comics
w/GUEST SPEAKER
SKETCH McLOUDMOUTH

THOSE THINGS DON'T *MATTER* -- WHAT MATTERS IS HOW YOU *SELL* THEM.

FLIP!

COMICS AREN'T *ABOUT* COMICS.

THEY'RE ABOUT *FRANCHISES*!

HOW CAN WE *SQUEEZE* THE MOST *MONEY* OUT OF THIS *ONE* IDEA?

COMIC

MERCHANDISING   LICENSING

SHIRTS & APPAREL   TOYS   MOVIES   TV

POSTERS & PRINTS   THEME PARKS

GOOD ARTISTS TOIL IN *OBSCURITY* THEIR WHOLE *LIVES* --

NEVER ACHIEVING ANY KIND OF *SUCCESS* OR *RECOGNITION*.

IF YOU'RE *LUCKY*, YOU MAY GET *ONE* BIG CHANCE -- SO *MILK* IT FOR ALL IT'S WORTH!

I THOUGHT THIS WAS ABOUT *TIME SHARES*?

COMIC

ORIGINAL IDEAS ARE HARD TO COME BY! **GOOD** ORIGINAL IDEAS EVEN MORE SO!

JUST FOLLOW WHAT PEOPLE ALREADY LIKE, AND THE **WORK** IS DONE FOR YOU!

SO, HOW DO YOU WANT TO **SELL OUT?**

MY INCREDIBLE COMIC

APPEALING TO THE **ADOLESCENT POWER FANTASY** NETS YOU FANS OF THE PEOPLE **SNEERED** AT FOR READING COMICS.

WOW THEM BY TAKING SOMETHING **GOOD** AND MAKING IT...

AWESOME!

COURT THE OBSESSIVE **MANGA** FAN WITH COMICS THAT INDULGE YOUR READERS' **WANDERLUST** FOR A FAR-FLUNG **FANTASYLAND** --

OR JUST THEIR REGULAR LUST FOR **SUBMISSIVE** HIGH SCHOOL GIRLS AND **ANDROGYNOUS** BOYS.

GET WEB 2.0 CRED BY FILLING YOUR STORIES WITH GODDAMN MEMES

PARROTING A WORN JOKE IS ALMOST AS GOOD AS AN ORIGINAL IDEA

OR AIM FOR LEGITIMACY BY FOLLOWING THE TROPES AND IRONIC **NEO-NOSTALGIA** OF THE **LITERATI** --

Bookbinder's Ironic Supply Store

826

ACME SMALL PRINT DIGEST

UNTIL YOU'RE USING TERMS LIKE "TROPES" AND "IRONIC NEO-NOSTALGIA" LIKE WE'RE ALL SUPPOSED TO **KNOW** WHAT YOU'RE **TALKING** ABOUT.

WHETHER YOUR READERS ARE **INTELLECTUALS**, OTAKU, OR IN A STATE OF **ARRESTED DEVELOPMENT**...

IF YOU **PANDER** TO YOUR FANS INSTEAD OF **CHALLENGING** THEM...

ART

MONEY

YOU MAY NOT BE MAKING **ART**... BUT AT LEAST YOU'LL BE MAKING **MONEY!**

MONEY

$

...AND THEN YOU CAN GET OUT OF COMICS FOR **GOOD!**

MISUNDERSTANDING COMICS

FUNDED! THIS PROJECT CONNED **222** PEOPLE OUT OF THEIR CASH ON AUG 12, 2012.

FUNDS RAISED
$1,234,067

BACKERS
20,198

DUE DATE
~~MAR~~ ~~APR~~ ~~MAY~~ ~~JUNE~~ ~~JULY~~ 2013

IF YOU'RE SMART, PEOPLE WILL THROW MONEY AT YOU -- AND YOU WON'T EVEN HAVE TO DO ANYTHING!

HEHE... SUCKERS!

EMAILED
SIGNED
MAILED TO YOU

FAN: AUTOGRAPHED COPY THE BOOK, PLUS THE PDF, STICKER, THANK-YOU POSTCARD, AND YOUR NAME IN THE THANK-YOU SECTION OF THE BOOK!

SPECIAL COLLECTOR
ANDREAS DANIELSSON

YOUTUBE VIDEO COLLECTORS
JACKIE THOMAS WOHLENHAUS • RELAXINGDRAGON

VANITY COLLECTORS
ADAM JUDA • AMANDA IRLE • ERIC BEHRENS • ERIC CHARLES • FEEFERS • HAYSTACKCALDOON • HONEY CUDDLES • KHATOBLEPAS • NUCLEARMIME • ROBERTA BRODSKY • SAMAEL THE BUTTERDRAGON • UDITVANU DAS

OBSESSED FANS
JACOB STRICK • JESS REYNOLDS • LUIGI • MATT KEELEY • SEAN MORRIS • VIREDAE MARCHETTE • XMINUSI

FANS
AARON VANEK • ABDULLAH SHAMSI • ALISA DIDKOVSKY • ALTHEA EMILY PERGAKIS-CRONE • ANDREA BIAGGI • ANDREW MIDDLEMAS • ANDREW SANFORD • AURELINA • BLAKE MIDDLETON • BRAD GARRETT • BRITTANY DUARTE • C. GLEN WILLIAMS • CHRIS KOLINA • COYOTZIN • CRAIG MILLER • DANIEL CUTLER • DANIEL PURCELL • DANNY DOUGHERTY • DAVIS • ED KOWALCZEWSKI • EDWIN DEAN • ERIC LERNOULD • GREGORY NORWOOD • HALEY MILLMAN • HAMID SIRHAN • HOLDEN CRICK • IRENE H. • JAMES BIRDSALL • JAMIE GAMBELL • JESSICA FURE • JESSICA WATKINS • JILL THOMPSON • JILLERS • JOHANNES BRAUN • JOHN M. SCRUDDER • JOÃO SILVEIRA • KALT • KATY KING • KEVIN FLANAGAN • KEVIN LAI • KITTY • KRIS LOUKAS • KRISTIAN BORUFF • LINDSEY SULLIVAN • LIZ COURTS • LUCASHOAL • MARIE S. • MARTHA CORNOG • MARY BETH PERSON • MASSON • MATT CZARNOWSKI • MATT MINER • MICHAEL KAPLAN • MIGHTY_BORLAUG • MILO REID • MOLLY PAPIN • NOAH RAMON • PHIL GIBSON • PHILIP SANT • POLLY • R LANG • RAPHAEL STORMAGEDDON SOOHOO • RICARDO ARREDONDO • RILEY BUCK • RISQUEMARIONETTE • RONNIERACCOON • RYAN POWER • RYAN SHELLITO • SPENCER • STEPH CHERRYWELL • TALBERT JOHNSON • TALLTALE • TATERPIE • TED ANDERSON • THE EVIL ALIEN ROBOTS CHARITABLE TRUST • THOM BLAKE • TPGARY • TYDE • ZACH P

VANITY C
(OR SOM
CHOICE) WILL B
CHARACTER IN   3RAPHIC
NOVEL! PLUS Y   LL RECEIVE
ALL PRIZES FF   THE OBSESSE
FAN REWARD

YOUT   OLLECTOR: WE MAKE FUN OF ANY ISSUE OF YOUR FAVORITE COMIC ON YOUTUBE. GOOD OR BAD, AS LONG AS WE CAN FIND IT, WE'LL RIP IT TO SHREDS.

SEQUELS, PREQUELS, SPIN-OFFS, AND A WHOLE ECOSYSTEM HAS SPRUNG UP -- ALL FROM THAT ONE SEED OF AN IDEA!

YOU'VE FOUND WHAT WORKS... SO WHY MESS WITH A GOOD THING?

UH-OH, I'M ALMOST OUT OF SHOCKING AND TRANSGRESSIVE IDEAS TO PISS OFF MY READERS!

...THE DUMB CUNTS.

HIT GRANNY

KICKIN' ARSE

...THEN THE WHORE PUNCHES THE MUSLIM'S TEETH IN!!

IT WOULD BE HOT IF SNOW WHITE HAD SEX WITH THE SEVEN DWARVES.

THIS REPETITION IS ALL PART OF A WINNING FORMULA!

MISUNDERSTANDING COMICS

MISMAKING COMICS

MISREINVENTING COMICS

AND THERE ARE AS MANY WAYS TO MILK THAT CASH COW AS THERE ARE STARS IN THE SKY!

BUT THAT WAS THE *PROBLEM* ALL ALONG -- THINKING COMICS WERE SOMETHING TO *ESCAPE*.

THESE ARE THE *FERTILE GROUNDS* WHERE NEW IDEAS TAKE *ROOT!*

NEW COMICS COME OUT EVERY *WEEK* -- WHERE ELSE CAN YOU TAKE AS MANY *RISKS* AND STILL REACH A WIDE AUDIENCE?

TO *IGNORE* THIS IS TO *MISUNDERSTAND* COMICS.

COMICS ONLY WORK IF YOU USE THEM TO PUSH *BOUNDARIES* -- TO BEND, BREAK, AND *EXPAND* THE RULES OF WHAT SEQUENTIAL ART IS *CAPABLE* OF.

I'VE SHOWN YOU THE TRICKS AND THE SHORT-CUTS -- SO YOU CAN *AVOID* THEM.

SO YOU CAN WRITE *BETTER* COMICS.

OR YOU CAN BECOME *JADED* AND *CYNICAL* AND HOLE YOURSELF UP IN YOUR ROOM,

WRITING BITTER SCREEDS ABOUT HOW COMICS *SUCK!*

. . . .

HUH.

DON'T FORGET TO BUY...

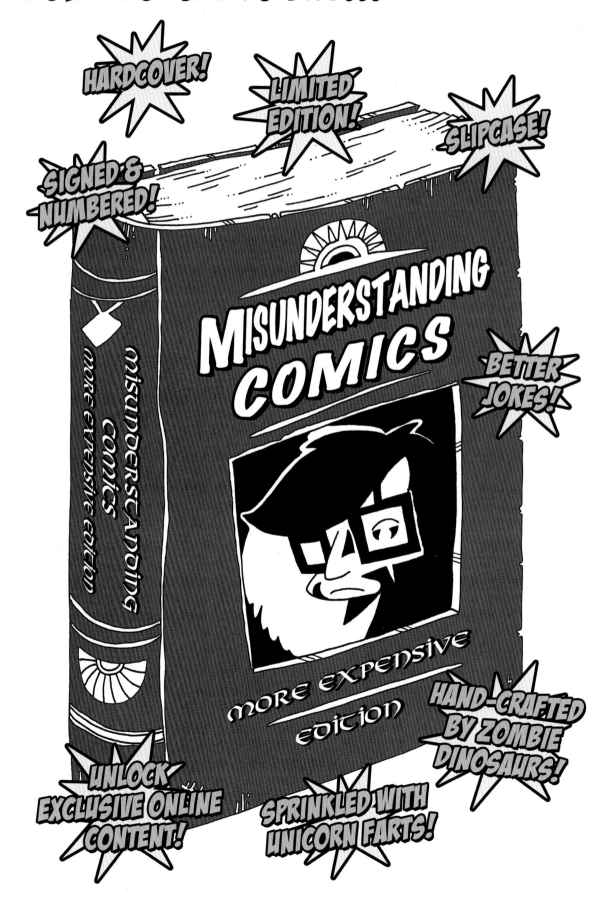